DESIGN CHALLENGE

Teacher's Book

to support
the design and technology series
DESIGN CHALLENGE

Keith Good

CW00734629

Contents

Introduction

This book is intended to help teachers and other adults using the *Design Challenge* series by giving background information, links with other subjects and practical hints. The copiable pages can be used to speed up the making of the core 'recipes', leaving more time for innovative design work and easing the teacher's task. As well as saving time, the photocopiable pages can also help to improve the quality of less able pupils' work in particular by helping them with measuring and marking out. Suggestions for using individual photocopiables are included in the page notes.

Design and Technology (D&T) contributes to the curriculum by preparing children to make creative changes to things around them and enabling them to participate in their changing technological world. The *Design Challenge* series encourages a creative approach and addresses some important aspects of design and technological knowledge and understanding. These include electrical circuits, mechanisms, structures and working with tools, materials and components. Pupils' awareness of health and safety issues is raised throughout the series as potential hazards and the need for adult help is indicated in the texts.

The 'recipes' in the pupil books are intended to introduce technology and promote success. Having something to handle and try out is a great help in stimulating pupils' ideas. Although reading through recipes is helpful, they are often easier to follow when the practical work is being completed stage by stage. One completed stage helps to provide clues for the next.

Developing, planning and communicating ideas are explicitly encouraged by the *Getting Ideas* sections. Getting pupils to generate design ideas is central to this series and to design and technology in general. Perhaps one of the first conditions needed is a climate where pupils feel that their ideas are valued. It is all too easy for adults to impose their own preconceived 'right answers' on children, however well-meant this may be. A child whose ideas are ignored or, still worse, ridiculed, is likely to spend his/her effort working out the teacher's 'right answer' rather than developing his/her own. In many subjects, the teacher does of course have the one right answer which the child has to work out. We need to establish that in D&T a child's ideas will be considered on their merits against the need, design problem or project brief. This is far from saying that all responses to a problem are equally good and that any will do. One of the strengths of D&T at its best is that pupils can examine and judge their solutions for themselves rather than only receiving an assessment from an adult.

D&T, done well, can be of tremendous educational value. It should also be fun! These books are intended to help on both counts.

Good D&T practice

Time and movement

Government initiatives and the pressure to deliver the national curriculum core subjects make it more important than ever to use D&T time to best effect. Establish priorities for written/graphic work – exploring, developing and explaining ideas should take priority over writing out how to make the core or 'what we did' step-by-step. Look out for the D&T potential in themes and activities while planning to deliver other subjects.

Unnecessary movement about the room wastes time and can increase the risk of accidents. Movement can be much reduced by using tool caddies or trays to transport most of the equipment that a group of pupils will need from a cupboard in one go. Colour-coding tools and carriers using small pots of modelling paints encourages pupils to take care of *their* equipment rather than making up their kit by taking any within reach. Involving pupils in designing an efficient and safe working environment, including how best to organise facilities, is very worthwhile.

Money

Design Challenge projects use free and cheap materials as far as possible. This means that what money is available can be reserved for things that must be bought e.g. electrical components. Shopping around and bulk-buying with neighbouring schools are other ways to make the budget go further. Involve children in comparing costs of materials, designing storage arrangements and rules for access. Good, well-presented D&T work can be used to encourage parent-teacher associations to raise money for things like computer control equipment. A cautionary note: the 'tool boards' and 'technology trolleys' in catalogues have their merits but can be an expensive way to buy tools. Explaining your needs to parents and the wider community can bring in all sorts of resources. Whatever you want, someone somewhere is probably throwing it away!

Display

D&T work has tremendous display potential. Audiences can interact with exhibits and make them work, as well as admiring their innovation and colour. *Amazing Machines* and *Exciting Electrics* and other working projects need to be seen in action to be fully appreciated. Encourage pupil involvement in designing interactive displays. Empathising with the viewer is good experience and there are plenty of opportunities for promoting literacy and ICT skills. Consider promoting D&T work by displaying it in the wider community e.g. a shop window, your local library and other schools, including the secondary schools where the children will go.

Liaison with parents and other schools

Many parents will be less clear about what is involved in D&T than they are about other subjects in the curriculum. To gain their support it is important to show parents the educational value of D&T work at every opportunity. A copy of the *Design Challenge Record Sheet* (page 48) sent home with practical work will help to explain what lies behind practical work. Stress the relevance to the world around children and their future. The introduction to each double page in the *Design Challenge* books relates the technology in the projects to technology in the wider world. It is worth stressing the design-based and problem-solving aspects of D&T to distinguish it from the craftwork that parents may have known. Plan homework to reflect the spirit of good D&T. Parents and children could be involved in *Design Challenge* activities as part of an Open Day or school fête.

Liaison with a secondary school D&T department can ease the move between schools for pupils and help to avoid duplication of projects.

Adult helpers

Classroom assistants and voluntary helpers have long played a part in the primary classroom and an extra 'pair of hands' is especially valuable in D&T. Publicising the nature of D&T work may help to attract helpers with enthusiasm and abilities. Because D&T is such a varied activity, a wide range of helper experience is relevant and useful. Helpers need to be well briefed so that they stimulate and encourage pupils' ideas rather than impose their own, however well intentioned this might be. It is helpful to distinguish between the 'cores' or 'recipes' in the *Design Challenge* series (where instructions are to be followed) and the *development* of cores where pupils' ideas must be given free play.

Do get a copy of the *Guide for Teacher Assistants*

from the Design and Technology Association DATA (see Useful addresses, page 28).

The D&T Co-ordinator

Anyone in this role should encourage their school to join the Design and Technology Association (DATA) which offers publications at reduced price and other benefits to members. Do get a copy of *The Design and Technology Primary Co-ordinators File* from DATA (see Useful addresses, page 28).

Using ICT

ICT is of increasing importance in society and the national curriculum reflects this. Some opportunities for using computers and enhancing pupils' projects through ICT are pointed out as they occur in the *Design Challenge* books. Pupils should be encouraged to look for ways to use ICT appropriately at each stage of a project, depending on the hardware and software available to them. For example:

● CD-ROMs can be used at the start of a project, for example to find out more about the technology that is introduced in the project and how it is used in the wider world. Looking at applications in different times and cultures will help to stimulate pupils' own ideas. The aim is inspiration rather than imitation.

● Spreadsheets could be used to handle information about preferences concerning a game that is being designed.

● ICT is an ideal way for pupils to produce text such as rules, scripts and captions, especially as revision and improvements are so easy to make. Graphics packages and clip-art offer similar advantages. Word-processed text and graphics can be added to projects for a professional look.

● Classroom computer control programmes (see page 5) can be triggered by all the switches in *Exciting Electrics.*

Recording and displaying work

Involving pupils in recording and presenting their work can be a valuable activity in its own right and the camcorder has particular uses in D&T.

Camcorders are ideal for recording mechanical toys, vehicles, puppets and other working projects from the *Design Challenge* series. Commercials could be made about projects such as breads and biscuits. Pupils could also make informative videos showing the stages that led to the finished project.

The bridges (page 16) and beams (page 9) in *Super Structures* can be videoed as they are loaded and tested to destruction. Video offers a unique way of seeing 'action replays' so that structures can be studied as they collapse.

Through video pupils can be shown developing and evaluating their work even when it is not convenient for them to be present, e.g. during a parent's evening or after school during an inspection.

Pupils enjoy recording their own work and this is a chance to develop ICT skills in a purposeful context.

Video offers a good way of interviewing 'clients' for design projects. Video is also ideal for 'before and after' shots where a design problem can be shown and then its solution. Videoing pupils designing and making for later analysis helps with sharing successes and problems with colleagues and could be valuable for staff development sessions.

About the books

NB: All page numbers in the following headings refer to the pupil's book in question.

1. Exciting Electrics

This book gives starting points for projects where electrics are central, but the ideas can also be used to enhance projects stimulated by other books in the series. Structures could have warning or signalling lights added, machines can be enhanced by buzzing and flashing lights.

Safety

Pupils must be made to understand that mains electricity can be lethal and that they must *never* tamper with it. This should in any case be part of their general 'keeping safe' education, but always stress that only batteries are to be used when introducing electrics.

Batteries should not be carried in pockets, incinerated or opened. Store batteries away from metal objects that might cause a short circuit. Covering the battery terminals with masking tape or PVC electrical tape is a good precaution against accidental short circuits during storage. Never attempt to recharge normal batteries. Pupils should not use rechargeable batteries. These can cause burns if short-circuited. (See also 'Make it Safe' by NAAIDT, page 27.)

Computer control

Computers control things all around us and pupils can use simple computer control in the classroom to create quite sophisticated effects. Adults may find it hard to accept that although classroom control packages may be unfamiliar, they are not intrinsically difficult! The following notes are just to stimulate interest. All packages come with full instructions.

With a suitable piece of hardware (an interface box) and the software that comes with it, most computers can be used to control any projects that include circuits. Control packages for classroom use are available from most of the suppliers shown on page 28. Valiant Technology (creators of the well-known *Roamer Robot*) has a particular emphasis on control technology. The simplest form of control works rather like a time switch. The user tells the computer to switch one or more *output* circuits (like those on pages 6 to 11 of *Exciting Electrics*) on and off. The computer remembers the sequence and runs the same program of switching on and off when a key is pressed. Once turning a component on and off for a period of time is mastered, very elaborate sequences (or *programs*) can be built up. Model disco lights, for example, could flash in a chosen pattern. A 'buggy' with a motor driving each of its two wheels could be 'taught' to drive round a maze. By switching on one motor at a time, the package could make the buggy turn. Some devices like Lego Dacta's *Control Centre* (which has two memories) are self-contained and don't need a computer, leaving it free for other work.

Some control packages also allow the computer to sense its environment through *input* devices like a pressure pad (page 12 of *Exciting Electrics*). Someone treading on the pressure pad could cause the computer to run the program of ON and OFF that it had been taught earlier. A model fairground of the future could be made to come to life when viewers tread on a large version of the pressure pad hidden under a mat.

NB All the switches in *Exciting Electrics* can be used with computer control packages that have INPUTS.

Electric circuits
Making series and parallel circuits – *pages 6 and 7*

As well as supporting the projects that follow, these two pages highlight the importance of electrical circuits and the basic requirements of successful ones. They introduce the important scientific knowledge that a complete circuit, including a battery or power supply, is needed to make any electrical device work, and show how to represent series circuits by drawings and diagrams.

● When batteries are in short supply, fix them at intervals around the room to allow pupils to test their circuits without undue movement or searching for a 'wandering' battery. When buzzers are in use, restricting access to a battery controls noise.

● Batteries are ruined very quickly by a *short circuit* i.e. if their positive (+) and negative (−) terminals are directly connected without something like a bulb or buzzer in between. While the battery is being drained in this way some heat is produced. Clipping the terminals of two 9-volt batteries together damages both of them at once! It is a good idea to warn pupils at the outset to avoid short circuits.

● To help pupils remember the layout of a *series circuit* (where one component follows another) it can be likened to a string of beads or a series of programmes. When only one component is being used, a series circuit works well enough, but as pupils will discover from the activities (page 7), adding more parts leads to disappointment. A *parallel circuit* can be likened to a railway track (with a red positive and a black negative rail) and components laid across like railway sleepers. Parallel circuits are very useful because they allow several components to work from one battery.

a series circuit

● The advantages of using symbols to draw circuits, and the uses of symbols in general for fast and accurate communication, are worth discussing.

Light, sound and movement
Designing circuits for your projects – *page 8*

Bulbs

Light is the cheapest output from a circuit. A 6-volt bulb will usually cope with a 9v battery – even if a fresh battery makes it rather bright! A 9-volt battery is likely to 'kill' a 3.5v bulb. Various bulb holders are available and these take either bulb. 3.5v and 6v bulbs are available and found in most schools, as they are used in science. The voltage is stamped on the bulb but it is often hard to read, so either have one kind only or keep them well apart. A dab of bright enamel paint or nail varnish is one way of distinguishing the two voltages. Get pupils to check that bulbs are fully screwed into their holders or they may not work.

LEDs

LEDs (light emitting diodes) are much cheaper and neater than bulbs and are more in scale with most projects. Usually red, green or yellow in colour, LEDs are widely used as indicator lights e.g. to tell you that the power is switched on to your stereo or that the caps lock on a computer is on. **Each LED used with a 9-volt battery must have a resistor or it will be ruined**.

Some interesting LEDs are available from electronics suppliers. Although more expensive than normal ones, they make impressive additions to projects. Flashing LEDs include a small microchip (visible as a black speck) and don't need an additional resistor when used with a 9-volt battery. Bi-colour (two colour) LEDs light up red or green depending on which way round the battery is connected. The lights on a motorised buggy could change colour when the buggy reverses. These LEDs are colourless/translucent when off and show that LEDs actually emit red or green light rather than just light up coloured plastic. LEDs can cope with 3 volts without a resistor.

Resistors

These small striped components restrict the amount of current flowing in a circuit or part of a circuit. They feature in *Exciting Electrics* as a means to protect LEDs from too much current from the 9-volt battery. The coloured bands on a resistor indicate the amount of electrical resistance it offers, measured in units called ohms. With the aid of a chart the colours can be converted into numbers. Resistors are often supplied joined to each other by paper strips to make them easy to load into mass-production machines in factories. Like other small parts they are easily lost so it is best to give them to pupils just before they join them into a circuit.

Buzzers

Piezo electric buzzers (usually in a round case) make a 'whistling' sound. Electromagnet buzzers (usually in a rectangular case) make more of a nasal bray!

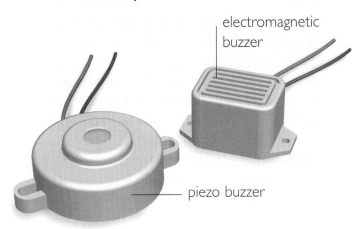

electromagnetic buzzer

piezo buzzer

An electrolytic capacitor will cause a buzzer (or light) to stay on for some seconds then fade. A capacitor gives a longer period of sound with the piezo electric buzzer. Large capacitors will keep the circuit working longer than small ones. Two or more smaller capacitors can be joined together at both ends (i.e. in parallel) to get the same effect. Remember that capacitors must be connected the right way round (+/−). The negative side is clearly marked on the case.

Motors

Don't expect too much turning force (*torque*) from small electric motors on their own. They often go too fast and deliver too little torque or turning power for many projects. Pulleys or gears are usually needed to increase torque and reduce speed. Plastic pulleys to fit on to motors can be bought from equipment suppliers (see page 28 of this book). Small motors with gear boxes can be salvaged from broken battery-powered toys. Motors drain batteries more quickly than the other components mentioned. A big benefit of electric motors is that they allow movement to be controlled using the computer control packages mentioned earlier.

More about making circuits
Joining wires and adding switches – *page 10*

The 9-volt battery connectors (sometimes called battery snaps) shown in *Exciting Electrics* are convenient and cheap. Nine-volt batteries are compact and provide plenty of power if several components are being used in the circuit. Should you want to use 1.5-volt batteries, 35mm film containers can be used as battery holders. Make a hole in the lid and bottom and use brass paper fasteners to make the terminals. Two containers joined by a paper fastener make a 3v battery holder.

Wire with lots of copper strands inside the plastic insulation is much more flexible and easier to twist to make connections than that with a single thick strand. Multi-strand wire also makes better connections when stapled on to pressure pads. Twisting wire on to paper clips first can help pupils make connections to bulb holders.

Encourage pupils to stick to the convention red wire for positive (+) and black wire for negative (-). This is a good opportunity to discuss the use of colour as communication rather than decoration. An electric motor can be made to spin the other way if the red and black wires from the battery to the motor are swapped over.

Wire strippers are designed for removing the plastic insulation from wires. (Do *not* allow the use of craft knives.) There are many different kinds of wire stripper. Some are easier to use than others - warn about sharp parts. If possible, get pupils to try (and evaluate) a variety of borrowed ones before buying some for class use.

Once a circuit is built into a project it can be very difficult for the pupil or teacher to spot any faults and a handful of tangled wires and components is little better. To minimise problems, have pupils build and test circuits that are fixed to a board with masking tape as suggested on page 10. A corrugated card board will do. This really helps to avoid guesswork, reduces mistakes and makes it easy to see any faults that do occur. Check that circuits work while they are taped to the board i.e. before they are installed in a project. Always encourage pupils to look for faults themselves before they ask for help.

Photocopiables: SHEET 1 The fault-finding checklist can be copied so that each pupil has one for reference. Mount on card and cover with sticky-backed plastic for durability.

Pressure pads
The pressure pad or membrane switch – *pages 12 to 21*

The pressure pad or membrane panel switch is a piece of modern technology that pupils can make and use creatively in a wide range of contexts. Made from thin layers, these switches are used on many appliances such as copiers and microwave ovens where their durability and lack of bulk are an advantage. Pupils can use pads to control anything that is battery-powered. It is best to start pupils on the simplest, on page 12.

Examples of uses
● a toy car turns on lights/opens garage door when pushed over the pad.

● a large switch helps partially sighted users.

● a dragon's eyes glow when its tummy is stroked.

- 'pin the tail on the donkey' type games (use Blu-Tack, not a pin).

- 'snakes and ladders' type games with pressure pads indicating hidden hazards.

For further inspiration - get pupils to explore the different ways of pressing the switch, e.g. head, elbows, feet, roll something over it, drop something on it, throw something safe at it.

Some practical tips

- Use glue sticks to fix the foil - this prevents pupils making 'glue sandwiches' by over-zealous use of white glue! Surplus glue that gets on the front of the foil can act as an invisible insulator. When joining foil strips, remind pupils to glue either side of the actual join rather than on it. Glue on the join can act as an insulator and stop the circuit working.

- The 'window' or hole in the basic switch can be built by sticking four strips together. Cut strips on a rotary paper trimmer. For large pads use thicker layers or the top layer may sag through the window and keep the switch on. This can also happen if over-large windows are cut in the switches shown. Add an extra layer with a 'window' or reduce the size of the window if pressure pads stay on.

- Test the switch before stapling the layers together. Small staplers are the easiest for pupils to use. Have them put the first staple tightly across the insulation for a good grip. Put the second staple tightly across the wire strands to make a good electrical contact. This prevents bare wires bending away from the foil, which stops the circuit working.

- Making examples of the recipe pads for pupils to copy is helpful. Cover these with sticky-backed plastic for durability. The creative part comes when pupils design

projects that use the switches, modify them or design their own to meet a need.

- Have pupils make the circuit and test it before cutting the wire to add the switch. In the event of a problem a circuit that worked before the switch was added indicates that it is the switch that needs attention.

- A sharp rotary trimmer (guillotine) cuts ribbons of foil well. Doing this for pupils saves time and waste and gives neat results. Scissors with fine serrations also cut foil well.

- The bottom layer of the basic switch can be used on its own as a piece of science equipment to test which materials conduct.

- The grids for the switches on pages 16 and 18 offer an opportunity to teach co-ordinates, which are relevant to Geography and Mathematics.

Photocopiables: SHEET 2 Make *two* copies of the grid provided for each pressure pad to save pupil time when making the pressure pad on page 16.

Photocopiables: SHEETS 2, 3 and **4** For each pressure pad on page 18 make ONE copy of the plain grid (2), ONE showing cut-outs (3) and ONE showing where foil tracks go (4).

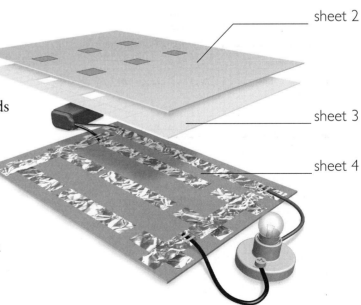

sheet 2

sheet 3

sheet 4

The push-to-break switch
A switch that is always on – unless you press it! – *page 22*

The working parts of commercially-made push-to-make (press for on) and push-to-break (push for off) switches are hidden but when pupils make their own they can see and understand how they work. The three switches can be made larger if that suits the project in hand. As with the pressure pads, put one staple tightly across the plastic insulation for a good grip and another across the bare wire for a good connection. Encourage pupils to think about how the switches could be turned on or off.

The reed switch
A switch that works without being touched – *page 24*

The inner workings of most components are hidden but the contacts in a reed switch can be seen closing when a magnet is brought near, especially if a hand lens is used. It consists of a sealed glass tube about 25mm long with a stiff wire sticking out of each end. Inside are two contacts that touch and turn on the switch when a magnet is brought close. How close the magnet needs to come depends on the strength of the magnet and which way it is facing. Pupils can experiment to find out for themselves.

Any battery-powered circuit can be switched on by passing a magnet close to the reed switch but note that they tend to stick on when used with motors.

Connecting strip (page 10) is the best way to join wires to the switch. This allows the switch to be turned until it works best with the magnet, and then held in position. Wires can be wound round and taped on to the switch as a second choice if connecting strip is not available.

Reed switches are simple to use and quite cheap. Used with imagination they are very versatile, opening up all sorts of possibilities. It is a good idea to draw attention to distinctive features of the reed switch i.e. it does not need to be touched and can be hidden under paper, fabric or thin card.

The many possible applications include:

● A magic wand with the obligatory magnet hidden in it, which could make all sorts of things happen, to the puzzlement of onlookers.

● Pat a model robot with a magnet between your fingers and watch its light-bulb eyes brighten in recognition.

● A creature or vehicle with a magnet underneath can set off an alarm if a line is crossed. As a model tractor tips too far, a pendulum inside swings, setting off a warning buzzer. Every time a wheel turns a light flashes or a bell rings.

Safety
Reed switches are made of glass and although they are quite robust they can be broken and this should be stressed to pupils. The wires coming from the switch must not be bent or the glass is likely to break, leaving sharp pieces.

The tilt switch
A switch that works when something moves – *page 26*

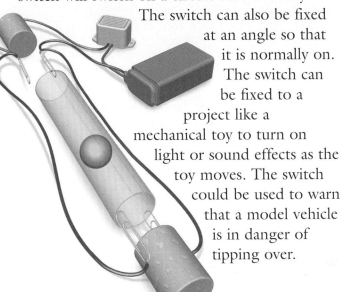

When fixed to something that moves, the tilt switch will switch on a circuit automatically. The switch can also be fixed at an angle so that it is normally on. The switch can be fixed to a project like a mechanical toy to turn on light or sound effects as the toy moves. The switch could be used to warn that a model vehicle is in danger of tipping over.

Cutting the plastic bottle to form the tube gives an opportunity for estimating the circumference of the corks and thinking of ways to measure this. Clear or pale green bottles give the best view of what is happening inside the switch. If corks are in short supply, one can be cut into two pieces with a fine-toothed 'junior' hacksaw. However, used wine corks are usually quite easy to come by.

Important: Remember not to use coloured paperclips. The coating on some acts as an insulator and the circuit won't work.

A coin-operated switch
Make your own slot machine – *page 28*

The basic switch design provided exploits the conductivity of metal coins to complete the circuit. By cutting a suitable sized hole in the slide, small coins could be made to drop into a reject box before they reach the foil strips and turn the circuit on. Pupils could be invited to think about what other usable properties coins have, such as weight and shape. A coin could roll down a v-shaped cardboard seesaw that tilts to bring switch contacts together. A spring-loaded platform could be put in the bottom of the collecting box. When sufficient weight of coins rest on the platform, it could be pressed down to bring two foil contacts together to complete a circuit. Strips of plastic bottle could be used to make springs for the platform. Different widths of plastic will collapse under different weights of coins.

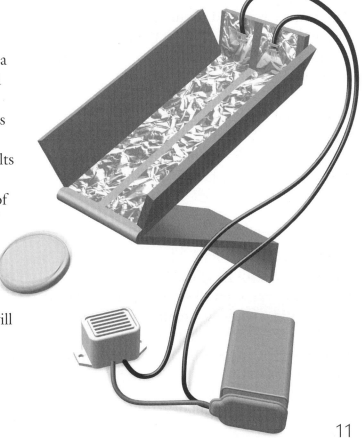

11

2. Amazing Machines

This book shows how to make mechanical toys and other devices using readily available materials - corrugated cardboard, plastic-coated garden wire and so on. Each project is based on a particular mechanism which is first shown used in everyday life. The content also relates to the science curriculum, e.g. forces and motion, friction, and to the maths curriculum, e.g. making 2D and 3D shapes and applying measuring skills in a range of purposeful contexts.

If you use 4mm diameter wooden dowel rod for machine parts this will fit the holes in the stout card disks that are available from suppliers. 5mm diameter rod can be used if the holes in the disks are stretched a little with the end of a biro pen. Cut the rod with a fine-toothed junior hacksaw while holding it securely in a small vice that cramps on to a table. Depending on their age and your judgement of the child you may do this for pupils or allow them to do this under supervision. Saw close to the vice. Keeping the saw straight prevents jamming. If a child cuts the dowel, this should be under supervision and with both hands on the saw to improve control – and keep the hands away from harm!

How to support your mechanisms
Three basic structures to support moving parts – *page 6*

Whether they are made from metal or cardboard, moving parts need a firm foundation to keep them in place if they are to work properly. Corrugated cardboard is readily available at no cost and is rigid but easy to work with. Large boxes can be flattened and stored in a plan chest or behind a cupboard.

One big cardboard box can be flattened out to make lots of project-sized structures. A photocopy paper box will make a structure for several machines. Boxes (and unfinished machines) can be stored flat to save space. Turning the box inside out hides any printing that would be difficult to cover with paint.

Cutting rectangles for the pupils using a rotary trimmer or guillotine speeds up the making and improves the quality.

Photocopiables: SHEET 5 Copy this support structure on to card and cover with sticky-backed plastic for durability. Cut out the notches and mark in them with a pencil to transfer sizes to corrugated cardboard.

SHEET 6 Use as above to make support structures for conveyor belts.

NB: Longer structures can be made by sliding the template to each end of card of any desired length. Taller and wider structures can made by enlarging the template on the photocopier.

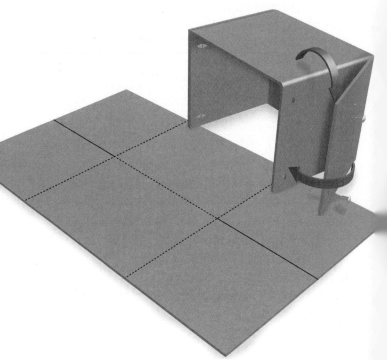

Making rolls, handles and guides
Ideas to help on many projects – *page 8*

The techniques shown on this page are used in many of the activities in *Amazing Machines* so they are worth teaching thoroughly. When the method was trialled with pupils they improved rapidly with practice. 'Limbering' the strips of card by pulling them tightly over a table edge makes rolling easier. A fairly 'sharp' rather than a rounded edge works best.

Some practical tips

● Put a little white glue on the end of a strip of card and hold it firmly round the rod between thumb and forefinger. Once the glue grips, move on to the others. This speeds things up.

● **Important**: leave the glue joints to dry fully before gluing one strip at a time and rolling it. Using too much glue is a common fault to watch for. Only a thin film is needed and this makes for rapid drying. This might be a good time to discuss evaporation, which is how water-based white glue sets.

● Roll strips tightly, trying to form flat-ended cylinders. This gives maximum gluing area for cams, disks and other parts later - this is important. Hold rolls firmly until the ends grip, then leave to dry well – putting them in a warm place speeds things up.

The card rolls are surprisingly strong and hard when thoroughly dry. They are also concentric with the rod and well bonded to it and provide a good fixing for other parts.

This technique was developed by the author to overcome a number of practical problems with traditional methods. Readers who have tried to get pupils to make working things using conventional methods and materials will appreciate the problems that can be encountered. For example, a tight hole in a wooden wheel leaves little room for glue, and glue cannot fill an over-large hole. Drilling or enlarging holes in wooden or mdf (medium density fibre board) wheels to fit wooden dowel rod involves more equipment and trouble than using the method shown.

Getting ideas
Exploring machines made by other people – *page 9*

Taking small unwanted products apart is a good way to find out how they work, and pupils may also get ideas and parts for their own projects. Pupils can be encouraged to spot the mechanisms shown in the book. Simple objects like clothes pegs show levers in use and it is interesting to compare different designs. Close observation can be encouraged by making exploded drawings that show parts as if moved apart. Model kit plans, repair and instruction manuals are full of examples of this kind of drawing. The copiable isometric grid (**SHEET 18**) used under copier paper will help with the

drawing and arranging the pieces. If there are lots of pieces, pupils can choose some that interest them. An adult could use a hot glue gun or epoxy resin adhesive to fix parts to a mounting board to show how they go together. Pupils could use a computer to make labels for the parts and to write about the product. They could be involved in designing a way to sort and store parts for future use.

Make sure that only *expendable* objects are explored - never assume that products can be reassembled to their original condition!

Levers and linkages
Simple moving parts for your mechanisms – *page 10*

These pages show how to make linkages for pupils to use in design projects e.g. lunging crocodile, mechanism for tipping the back of a model lorry, shadow puppets. There are three ways of arranging the load, effort (input force) and fulcrum (pivot), giving what is known in physics as first class (EFL) levers, e.g. pliers, second class (ELF) levers, e.g. a wheelbarrow and third class levers (LEF) e.g. tweezers.

● For more durable holes, tape a piece of plastic bottle over the hole and pierce.

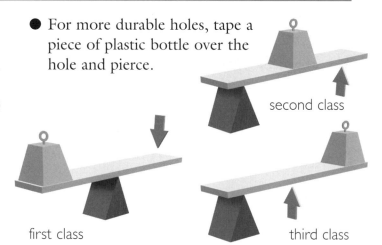

second class

first class

third class

Crankshafts
Moving parts to and fro and up and down – *page 12*

Making a full-sized drawing of the crankshaft can help to make sure it is the right length and doesn't jam against the support structure. The drawing can be made on the top of the structure or on paper, having drawn round the structure. Remember to allow for the width of the corrugated card that will be threaded on to the crankshaft. The drawing can be used to work out the total length of wire needed (allow a little extra for the bends) and as a template for bending the plastic-coated wire to the right size and shape. Holding the wire with one pair of pliers and bending it with another is helpful, or the wire can be held in a small vice. Try to have an imaginary straight line (or axis of rotation) running through the crankshaft as this will help it to turn smoothly. Long lengths of wire pose more of a hazard than pieces cut to the length needed. Cut wire to length for pupils. Curling the end over makes using it safer, as does wearing goggles and working with arms straight to keep wire away from the face.

Working out the total length of wire needed is an example of how this kind of work gives pupils a chance to use and apply mathematics in practical tasks and real life problems.

Pulleys
Using wheels to make parts move – *page 14*

Pulleys are used for transferring rotary motion from one shaft to another, and increasing and decreasing speed. Pulleys have also been used for thousands of years to make it easier to lift heavy weights – physics books give more information about this.

The drum of a tumble drier acts as a large pulley which is driven by a small pulley on the motor. To transmit more torque or turning force, two or more pulleys and belts can be used to turn the shaft. Several pulleys of different size can be fixed to each other. Practically, getting the belt tight enough is important.

Gear wheels
Changing speed and direction – *page 16*

Although gears can be traced off from page 17, photocopying on to thin coloured card speeds up gear-making and reinforces the corrugated card teeth. The photocopier can also be used to reduce or enlarge the gears provided. Glue the photocopy to corrugated card before cutting them out. When making extra-strong, thick gears by gluing a number of gears together it is a good idea to have the tubes inside the card running at right angles to those on the next layer.

Photocopiables: SHEET 7 Glue photocopy to corrugated card *before* cutting out.

Friction drive
One part turns another by rubbing against it – *page 19*

This method is easier than using gears to transfer rotary motion through 90 degrees. Pupils can try adding abrasive paper, rubber and other materials to increase friction and so the amount of torque or turning force that can be delivered without the parts slipping. Plastic bottle springs can also be used to increase the amount of torque – see page 18. Adding the weight of clay or salt dough figures (*Moulding Materials* page 7) is another way of increasing torque.

Make sure pupils put the upright part in *before* they add the horizontal shaft – this is much easier and avoids forcing and possible breakage.

Cams
From round and round to up and down – *page 20*

Cams are much used in mechanical toys and other machines for converting 'round and round' movement into 'up and down'. Different cams are easily made to create different movements. Make sure pupils put the upright part (the follower) in before they add the horizontal shaft - this is much easier and avoids forcing and possible breakage.

A cam can be fixed to each end of a card roll to save time. Make the roll long enough to space the cams where they are needed. A lever can also be used as a follower. This will produce oscillating motion (movement to and fro in an arc).

The cam and friction drive mechanisms as shown on pages 19 to 21 rely on gravity so the parts that are moved have to be vertical. To add parts that work horizontally, cut a slice of a small plastic bottle 1-2cm wide. Squash the ring of bottle and make a hole through both layers with a paper punch to make a spring. Thread the spring on to the rod of the part to be moved. The strength of the spring can be adjusted by using a wider strip of plastic or cutting some of the spring away. One cam or friction drive roller can be made to move both a vertical and a horizontal part at the same time.

Putting cams and friction drive together – *page 21*

Combining these mechanisms adds interest to machines because of the variety of movement.

Wheels and axles...
Building a vehicle – *page 22*

Wheeled vehicles are vital to civilisation and feature in many topics and stories. Windlasses (where a rope round a shaft or wheel is used to haul or lift) are often used on sailing ships to raise sails and lift anchors. Science opportunities include looking at friction, air resistance and the knowledge that when springs and elastic bands are stretched they exert a force on whatever is stretching them. This is also an opportunity to consider the concept of lubrication to make the axles turn as freely as possible.

The basic chassis needs stiffening to prevent it bending when the elastic band is stretched. This can be done by adding layers (as mentioned in the text) but there are other ways and some useful opportunities for structures work. *Super Structures* in this series will give some ideas: try pages 8 to 9 on beams. Get pupils to explore the effect of different running surfaces e.g. polished floor, carpet, playground.

Pupils who go further and make part of the back axle thicker by adding a roll of card (see page 8), should feel that the string wrapped round the thicker part is easier to pull than that wrapped round the axle itself because the windlass gives a mechanical advantage. An even larger card roll would give an even easier the pull. Glue pegs on top of the existing ones so that a larger roll doesn't rub against the chassis.

Conveyor belts
Moving things along – *page 24*

A long conveyor belt may need extra rollers or a card support to stop it sagging too much.

To allow slides and chutes to be made steeper, the conveyor belt can be raised on books or a box. Textiles also make good conveyor belts, especially stretchy fabrics. Glue sandpaper (usually made from ground-up glass these days) to the driving roller for a really good grip.
Photocopiables: SHEET 6

Adding electrics
Making your machines do more – *page 26*

When the mechanisms move they can be made to switch on bulbs, buzzers and other electrical components. This adds another dimension and new possibilities to any mechanism in the book e.g. as a monster's head rises, the eyes light up. Pupils can experiment with different numbers and widths of foil strips on the roller. A larger roller could also be tried. Able pupils can try to synchronise the electrical circuit being on with the movement of the mechanism. (see *Exciting Electrics.*)

Amazing machines
Putting different mechanisms together – *page 28*

Many of the machines we use in real life are a collection of basic mechanisms working together. Able pupils can make sophisticated machines by combining two or more mechanisms from the book. An example of this is shown on page 21 where friction drive and cams work on one rod. The design of the supporting structures allows parts like camshafts to be taken out so that other mechanisms can be added to it. An easy way to get extra moving parts is to fix cotton threads to loosely pivoted or hinged parts. When the main mechanism moves, the threads tug parts and cause them to move. Pupils will need to experiment to find the correct thread length.

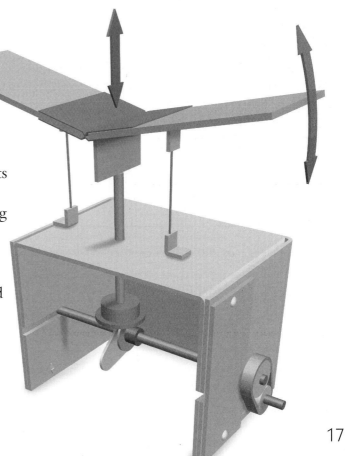

3. Super Structures

This book gives an understanding of the principles that underlie the structures that pupils live in, sit on, walk over and generally rely on every day. Correct terminology is taught and explained as the need for it occurs. Pupils really experience basic principles as they work on projects which draw on their own ideas and imagination. The content also relates to the science curriculum e.g. 'compare everyday materials....relate these properties to everyday uses' and 'forces'.

To establish the importance of structures, pupils could be told that their skeletons are structures that support the softer parts of their body. The chair they are sitting on and the building they are sitting in are structures too. Pupils could make a display to show how important and varied structures are. They could separate natural and made structures or put pictures of similar structures together. A tortoise shell could go with a cycle helmet!

Links with science include encouraging systematic enquiry, using focused exploration and investigation to acquire scientific knowledge, understanding and skill, planning experimental work and obtaining and considering evidence.

Materials and forces
Testing the strength of materials – *page 6*

These activities give pupils experience of the different forces that structures may have to withstand e.g. bending, squashing, stretching and shear force. Paper and card are good subjects for testing as they are very strong when pulled (in tension) but very much weaker when twisted (in torsion). Designers at any level have to consider how different materials react to forces and choose the best one for the job in hand. Discussing inappropriate uses for materials is a fun and quite quick way of highlighting their properties and the demands of different applications. 'As much use as a chocolate fireguard' could be the starting point for making up similar sayings. The language we use to describe materials can also be explored e.g. 'brittle' 'ductile' 'tough'. Good opportunities for science work e.g. grouping and classifying materials.

Beams
Making strong shapes – *page 8*

This is another opportunity to establish the concept of a fair test, which is important in science as well as D&T, and to explore how the shape of a piece of material greatly affects its ability to support itself or carry loads. Once pupils have established by experience which shapes are strong, they can be encouraged to look for tubes, corrugations, box sections and so on in furniture and other structures around them. The environmental benefits of using materials efficiently can also be discussed.

Strong shapes
Triangles and shells – *page 10*

Making rigid frames and triangulation can also be explored using construction kits with strips that have holes in them. Note that few things change their name when turned the other way up but the strut (shown on page 11) being compressed by the load becomes a tie when the bracket is turned over so that it is being stretched (in tension). Triangulation and shell structures are important in the everyday world and pupils can be encouraged to look for examples. Pupils will notice that cutting off the flat base of bubble packing reduces its strength, especially when it is pressed from the sides. The bubble pack game is a chance to re-use material that would otherwise be wasted and encourages looking at things in a fresh light. ICT is an ideal way to produce professional-looking small text (e.g. rules) on the back of the game. A paper punch can be used to make coloured disks from thin plastic or coloured card for playing parts. Note that domes are also shell structures. They feature on page 20 of *Moulding Materials*.

Stable structures
Testing shapes on a test ramp – *page 12*

To save time and materials, one test rig can be used by a small group of pupils to test structures they have designed, one of them acting as recorder. For another activity on the theme of stability, ask pupils to design small paper or thin card structures and compare their wind resistance (using a hair dryer). **Safety:** use hair dryer under supervision and set on cold. Which model buildings blow over most easily? This could lead on to a consideration of the airflow-directing devices on lorry cabs and racing cars.

Get pupils to look for and collect pictures of stable structures. Some structures, like road signs, are only stable when fixed into the ground. Humans are unstable structures because of their small base (the feet) and because a lot of their weight is at the top (the head). When pupils are designing their baby-shopping-toddler carrier, they could look at existing designs in catalogues and advertising. Encourage them to explore radical ideas rather than copy existing ones, which they should look at critically. Have they seen parents or other adults struggling with a baby buggy? They could discuss the problems with existing designs and show their own ideas.

Equilibrium
Balancing forces to keep things up – *page 14*

Pupils have experience of balancing forces from using see-saws and a table-top version could be made from a ruler to reinforce this. Pupils should notice that the position of the weight matters, not just the amount. Encourage them to look for pictures and actual examples of structures where forces have been balanced to keep a structure up. The long box with the hidden weight balances when it appears that it should not. This helps draw attention to the importance of weight distribution.

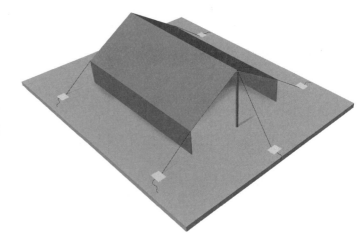

The soft structures are easier to make if two pupils co-operate. A full-sized tent (non frame) would give some good hands-on experience of using parts in tension. The suggested activities - the 'radio mast' and tent-type structures - bring together experience of triangulation, strong cross sections, stability etc. in a fun context.

Bridges
Bridging gaps with strength and stability – *page 16*

Bridges offer an opportunity to discuss the concept of a fair test and also symmetry and the need for accurate measurement. Cutting parts for bridges is a good opportunity to try a production-line approach where pupils collaborate. Get them to devise ways of improving speed and accuracy of production. Spaghetti is chosen because it is cheap, available and above all brittle! Is white or wholemeal pasta strongest? How can pupils find out? Avoid the use of crushed artstraws, which are weakened, and tell pupils not to crush them during building. For larger structures at little cost, tubes of newspaper can be formed round wooden dowel rod and glued. Once the paper is stuck the rod can be removed and the tubes joined with paper fasteners.

Make sure bridges testing is supervised and safe. Some model bridges will take a surprising amount of weight. This is made easier by having the whole class watch each test and is a chance to discuss the different designs and quality of manufacture.

When exploring arch bridges, 'steeper' and 'flatter' arches can be tried and compared. The curve made by a flexible cord or chain when it is held at each end (called a *catenary*) gives a good arch shape. Self-hardening clay can be used to make more realistic pieces (*voussoirs*) for the arch but this does involve drying time.

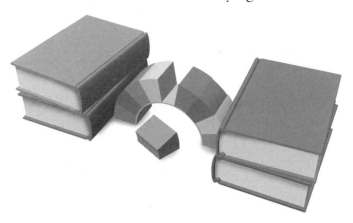

Photocopiables: SHEETS 8, 9, 10 and 11 Slip sheets inside clear plastic pocket files stiffened with corrugated card to make re-usable, non-stick and easily moved building boards for bridge sides and arch pieces.

Domes
Exploring rounded shapes – *page 20*

These pages show how to make a dome and design a model building based on it. Papier mâché domes also make a useful basis for hats and helmets for history topics and drama. Circle cutters are available that work on the principle of a compass with a blade rather than a pencil. The heavy-duty version is ideal for cutting a perfect circle for holding the balloon former. The sharp blade means that teachers may prefer to cut the circle for their pupils. A free corrugated card wheel comes with every hole!

Structures that collapse
Designing structures that fold flat – *page 22*

This is a chance to look at everyday things such as pushchairs and ironing boards that need to be collapsible. Designing something to meet apparently conflicting needs such as rigidity and collapsibility often poses interesting design challenges. These pages encourage pupils to use the given structures creatively. Imagining the structures made on different scales opens up a much wider range of possibilities. Able pupils could try to design their own structures that can collapse.

Pop-ups
Structures that seem to vanish – *page 24*

A pop-up is a self-erecting three-dimensional structure formed by opening a fold; other features like lift-up flaps are often added. Structures that appear and 'vanish' like magic have a wide appeal. Pop-up books can be shown and pupils could design their own, including word-processed text. Pop-up cards are sometimes suggested and although these can be done well, at worst the design element can be minimal e.g. sticking on a heart and writing 'Happy Mother's Day'. Games have lots of potential even for able pupils and formulating unambiguous rules presents a real challenge. Lots of other pop-up starting points can be found in the books dedicated to the subject.

Photocopiables: SHEETS 12 and 13 Copy on to coloured card.

Structures that protect
Designing packaging for fragile objects – *page 26*

Encourage pupils to make a collection of natural and manufactured protective structures. This helps establish how important they are and may stimulate their own designs. Packaging also offers an opportunity to discuss green issues and over-packaging. Packages should as far as possible be dropped to land flat on their bottom as biscuits dropped on their edge are surprisingly tough. Higher drops should be carried out by an adult. Pupils could develop the project e.g. adding a tail to the box, devising a square tube to guide it or some other way of ensuring that the package lands on its bottom. Provided they are kept clean e.g. handled with clean hands, broken biscuits can still be eaten. 'Refrigerator cake' can be made with adult help by melting chocolate in a water bath and stirring in the broken biscuits and other ingredients like raisins. The mixture is poured into moulds and set in the refrigerator. As with any food activity, there is a need to be aware of hygiene and food allergy issues and a parental consent form could be considered.

Photocopiables: SHEET 14 Copy on to coloured card.

Containers
Resisting forces from inside – *page 28*

ICT opportunity - decorative paper for the bag could be designed on a computer for a professional look. *Copy* and *paste* commands can be used to produce repeating patterns and an A4 printout can be enlarged to A3 using a photocopier before colouring. If only an A4 colour printer is available, motifs, texts and other designs can be cut out and fixed to the bag using a glue stick to prevent buckling.

Photocopiables: SHEET 15 Copy on to A3 paper. Coloured or pre-decorated paper could be used for final versions.

4. Moulding Materials

This book encourages pupils to design and make with a variety of mouldable materials, including some that can be eaten. Time for D&T is short so using materials that are quick and easy to shape is advantageous. Designs can be changed easily and different possibilities explored quickly. Moulding is often by far the easiest way of producing rounded shapes like figures and animals. Carving shapes from a block of material would be far slower, more hazardous and difficult. Many of the projects in *Amazing Machines* could be enhanced using moulded figures. When materials need time to harden, pupils should be encouraged to plan their work so that this time is used productively. Air-drying clay, for example, will dry without being watched! The drawing techniques shown in this book can help with all projects in the *Design Challenge* series. The opportunities for covering some of the science curriculum, e.g. materials and their properties, helps to make the time spent go further. Edible moulded projects have a special appeal. They also allow hygiene, kitchen safety and allergy issues to be raised. The Chartered Institute of Environmental Health's one-day Basic Food Hygiene Certificate course is recommended (see *Useful addresses*). Mouldable materials have been used for a long time in school and children enjoy them. This book links these important and easily worked materials with a designing, problem solving approach.

Introducing mouldable materials
Making a display – *page 6*

The variety of mouldable materials and moulded products (from bricks to bread and glass) makes it quite easy for pupils to create an interesting display. Encourage pupils to highlight what is special about mouldable materials in general, e.g. they are often cheap, easy and quick to shape. They can then move on to present individual materials highlighting the work they have designed and made. The ingredients that make up soft and baked dough can all be shown. Encourage the collection of a good range of moulded products to help establish their importance – plastic items are especially easy to find. Because mouldable materials can be shaped so easily without tools the audience could be given some hands-on experience. Encourage pupils to design different ways of presenting information so that they can select the best. Encourage maximum appropriate use of ICT (see *Further reading*).

Perishable products and materials may need to be shown as illustrations. Edible materials may need protection! Designing a mouldable materials display offers opportunities for links with *Exciting Electrics*. For example, pressure pads can be pressed to indicate the viewers' answers to questions about materials.

Making mouldable materials
From plaster to papier mâché – *page 7*

Some materials are potentially messy so cover the working area with plastic sheet and have pupils wear plastic aprons to protect their clothing.

Perhaps the least familiar material described is the foam plastic sheet. This is a polythene sheet filled with bubbles of nitrogen. It contains colouring but no other additives. Being a thermoplastic it can be repeatedly softened by gentle heat and moulded. It is much easier to cut and moulds at lower temperatures than acrylic (common brand name 'Perspex'), a plastic often used in secondary schools. The sheet can be ordered from suppliers such as those mentioned on page 27. Pupils can be encouraged to look for moulded plastic products in the world around them.

Safety
Since an oven is used to raise the plastic to moulding temperature, careful adult supervision is needed to avoid heating at too high a temperature or for too long. Use an electric oven only. Other mouldable materials (often branded products) can be found in Art and D&T suppliers, catalogues which give details about them. It is worth experimenting with small quantities.

Drawing
Modelling your ideas on paper – *page 10*

Basic drawing techniques are an important way to develop and express design ideas. Grid underlays make drawing easier. Pupils (and adults) often say that they 'can't draw' but like other skills, controlling a pencil improves with plenty of practice of the right kind. Pupils who find drawing difficult tend to concentrate on the pencil point but focusing on the 'target' and using the peripheral vision (or 'corner of the eye') to monitor the pencil is one of the 'tricks'.

Most designed objects are made up of a limited number of ingredients such as cubes, cylinders and spheres and these need practice. Pupils might be reminded that other skills such as riding a bicycle that they have mastered needed practice. All the illustrations in the *Design Challenge* series were first drawn by the author using a 'pump action' pencil with B or 2B leads. Using leads softer than the usual HB gives a good dark line with little pressure that photocopies well and is easy to rub out. Drawings help pupils to think and provide valuable evidence of their ideas for record keeping and assessment.

Photocopiables: SHEET 16 Use the square grid under photocopy type paper to help draw objects 2D, showing one side at a time (sometimes known as *orthographic* drawing). Drawing lines off at 45° converts 2D views into 3D (*oblique* drawing).

Photocopiables: SHEET 17 Use circle sheet as underlay to help adding of circles to drawings made as above. Mark axis lines faintly on first drawing to help positioning.

Photocopiables: SHEET 18 Use the isometric grid under photocopy type paper to help draw 3D objects.

Photocopiables: SHEET 19 Use the ellipse and cylinder sheet as an underlay to add these shapes to isometric drawings. Mark axis lines faintly on first drawing to help positioning.

Moulding by hand
Pots, cord pulls and zip pulls – *page 12*

Hands are wonderfully sensitive and versatile tools that can be used directly on soft materials. They are especially good for shaping objects like cord pulls that will be held in the hand.

Plasticine can be used to explore the forms that can be made by hand without it drying out or hardening. Moulding materials by hand allows pupils to experience them directly.

Rolling stamping and marking
Making shapes and decorating them – *page 14*

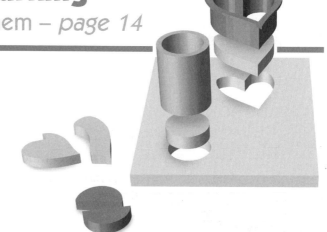

Like other processes in this book rolling, stamping and marking can be seen in everyday products. Coins, metal bottle caps etc could be collected for display. Stamping is a process that lends itself to mass production, allowing this important concept to be discussed.

Extruding mouldable materials
Making a minibeast – *page 16*

This process involves pushing material through a shaped hole. Toy plastic 'dough factories' are useful for showing the principle of extrusion. They produce a range of cross-sections, provided the material is soft enough. The

moulded lengths can be cut up to mass-produce decorative shapes. Encourage pupils to look for extruded products such as those suggested on the page.

Casting

Making models with moulds – *page 18*

Casting is another technique that can be used for mass production. Pupils could make different versions of their electronic product of the future from the same mould. One mould can be used by a number of pupils. Variations in the controls and other details as well as the instruction manuals mean that one mould can be used to make different projects. A card display stand could be designed to support and promote the product that has been designed. Modelling an electronic product of the future allows pupils to design without being limited by what they can make work. Links with science are that heating and cooling materials can cause them to change and that some changes can be reversed and some cannot. History link: casting iron and steel was an important part of the Industrial Revolution and also a prominent process in Victorian times. Encourage pupils to look for things that have been cast e.g. cast iron

street furniture, ice cubes and chocolate bars.

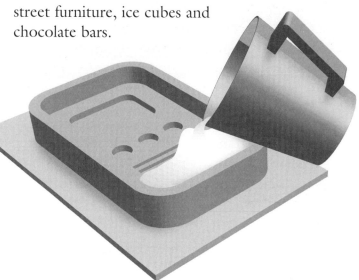

Product modelling is an important part of the industrial design process. Many of the products we use each day first existed as non-functioning models that allowed designers and their clients to assess a design and avoid expensive mistakes.

Hollow moulding

Making puppets for a play – *page 20*

Hollow mouldings not only weigh much less than a solid form of the same size, they also use much less material. Although papier mâché features on these pages, the process is similar to making polyester resin (fibreglass) mouldings for boats, car body shells and other products. Papier mâché has been used for furniture in the past.

The hollow space can be useful for storing, hiding or containing things. Puppets occur in many forms and in many cultures. Puppetry is a good medium for exploring human behaviour. Older pupils can prepare performances for younger children. Pupils can also design simple puppet theatres (a structures project) and include LEDs and other electrical features in their puppets. Many blockbuster films have used sophisticated puppets and this can be a point of interest for pupils. Strong links are possible with language, literacy and the arts. There are many books on puppetry and The Puppet Centre Trust, London is a good source of ideas and information, see page 28 for address.

Remember not to use wallpaper paste that contains fungicide to make papier mâché. Cutting a moulding to remove the Plasticine former needs a sharp craft knife and this should be done by an adult with care. A junior hacksaw could be used if the moulding is a thick one.

Moulded containers
Designing practical packages – *page 22*

This is a chance to encourage pupils to take a fresh look at things that most of them see, use and take for granted everyday. The design of shower gel, shampoo and similar containers has to combine aesthetics (look and feel) and consumer appeal with function. Some designs include working features like clips for hanging in the shower, Braille markings and non-drip openings. Get pupils to make a collection of containers, look at them critically and think of ideas and improvements for their own designs. Travel or complimentary hotel versions could be made (saving material as they are smaller). Cardboard structures could be designed to hold the give-away products, these could reflect the name and area of a new hotel. An imaginary potion could be contained perhaps exploiting links with literature e.g. George's Marvellous Medicine by Roald Dahl. Designing labels offer a good ICT opportunity and a chance to discuss bar codes, ingredients and consumer protection.

Safety

Ensure that containers to be examined are well washed out beforehand. **The hazard in some products used in the home could be discussed.**

Decorating people with mouldings
Making some jewellery – *page 24*

Looking at jewellery and other forms of body decoration offers a good opportunity to look at materials, as most have been used in this context, from stone and steel to feathers.

People of all times and cultures have adorned themselves so there are many historical and multicultural opportunities to explore.

Moulding more things to eat
Biscuits and bread with a difference – *page 26*

Moulded food products are common in everyday life. This is a good opportunity to design personalised presents.

Safety

Hygiene rules must be carefully observed when designing and making biscuits and breads from the basic recipes. As with any food activity, there is a need to be aware of food allergy issues and a parental consent form should be completed in advance, to alert the supervising adult to any potential problems. Adult supervision when using ovens, and the use of proper oven gloves, is essential.

Further reading

Make it Safe – Safety guidance for the teaching of Design and Technology at Key Stages 1 and 2 National Association of Advisers and Inspectors in Design and Technology 1992 ISBN 0 906457 07 (see *Useful addresses*)

DATA (see *Useful addresses*) The journal of the Design and Technology Association, recommended for very up-to-date information, articles, reviews and research. Contact DATA for details of many other useful publications that are available at reduced price to members.

Good, K., & Good, D., **Textile Technology for KS1 & KS2** Technology Teaching Systems Ltd 1996, ISBN 1 899413 30 8 (see *Useful addresses*)

Quality through Progression in Design and Technology NAAIDT (National Association of Advisers and Inspectors for Design and Technology) 1998 ISBN 0 906457 165 Available from NAAIDT Publications c/o DATA (see *Useful addresses*)

Neale, S., **Using Information Technology in Design and Technology**, Evans Brothers 1999, ISBN 0 237 51816 3

Talking About Information & Communication Technology in Subject Teaching – KS1&KS2 Canterbury Christ Church University College 1998 ISBN 1 899 253 40 8

Useful addresses

The University of Greenwich
The University of Greenwich's Avery Hill Campus, London has a long tradition of producing teachers and is an important provider of Design and Technology teachers in the UK. The lecturing team has also worked in Europe, USA, and South Africa and is interested in further contact with other countries.

Courses include an innovative award-winning collaborative project in which students work as a team to meet the needs of a client in the community. Among the many clients have been disabled people, nurseries and a conservation field centre. All courses include the opportunity to work outside the UK with one of our European partners. Students from Europe and beyond are very welcome to enquire about our courses.

In-service education and training
We offer D&T INSET to those teaching children of any age phase. Courses can be planned to particular requirements. We also offer an in-service masters degree MA with a range of education options including Technology Education. Our higher degree programme has already had a large number of graduates in other countries including Sweden and the Netherlands.

Display and resource material
Colourful graphic materials have been developed from student design and project work. The material is intended to stimulate teaching and learning and has proved popular with secondary schools and colleges in the UK. Please contact us for an illustrated brochure.

➡️

To enquire about any of the above, or for further details please contact:

Keith Good (Senior Lecturer)
The Centre for Design and Technology
University of Greenwich
Avery Hill Campus
Bexley Road
LONDON SE9 2PQ

Fax: +44 (0)208 331 9504
e-mail: k.w.good@gre.uk

Visit The University of Greenwich Design and Technology website:
www.gre.ac.uk/~eduweb/d&t.htm

Technology Enhancement Project (TEP)
www.tep.org.uk
A springboard to a range of useful websites.

Cabaret Mechanical Theatre
33/34 The Market
Covent Garden
London WC2E 8RE
www.cabaret.co.uk/start.htm
Inspirational automata exhibition with shop selling videos, cut-out automata and other resources.

The Puppet Centre Trust
Battersea Arts Centre
Lavender Hill
London SW11 5TN
For detailed information on everything to do with puppets, including extensive further reading.

Design and Technology Association (DATA)
16 Wellesbourne House
Walton Road
Wellesbourne
Warwickshire
CV35 9JB
www.data.org.uk
The main organisation for the subject in the UK but also internationally orientated.
Producer of many useful resources.
Discount prices for members.

The Centre for Alternative Technology
Education Department
Machynlleth
Powys SY20 9AZ
www.cat.org.uk

The Centre Support Team
CIEH
Chadwick Court
15 Hatfields
London SE1 8DJ
Information about food safety courses.

Consumer Information and Education Manager
Meat and Livestock Commission
Winterhill House
Snowdon Drive
Milton Keynes MK6 1AX
For a range of colourful free food-related resources

Technology equipment suppliers:

Valiant Technology Ltd.
Valiant House
3 Grange Mills Road
London
SW12 0NE
www.valiant-technology.com

Technology Teaching Systems Ltd (TTS)
Monk Road
Alfreton
Derbyshire
DE55 7RL
www.tts-group.co.uk

Commotion
Unit 11
Tannery Road
Tonbridge
Kent TN9 1RF

Heron Educational Ltd
Carrwood House
Carrwood Road
Chesterfield
S41 9QB
www.heron-educational.co.uk

Fault finding

What to do if your circuit doesn't work

Before you ask for help, look carefully at your circuit:

1. Check that the **battery** is working. Try it on a spare buzzer or light.

2. Check that all the parts are in **the right place and connected the right way** round.

3. If a circuit that used to work stops working, **see if something has come loose.**

4. If your circuit still doesn't work, **ask for help.**

Fault finding

What to do if your circuit doesn't work

Before you ask for help, look carefully at your circuit:

1. Check that the **battery** is working. Try it on a spare buzzer or light.

2. Check that all the parts are in **the right place and connected the right way** round.

3. If a circuit that used to work stops working, **see if something has come loose.**

4. If your circuit still doesn't work, **ask for help.**

Fault finding

What to do if your circuit doesn't work

Before you ask for help, look carefully at your circuit:

1. Check that the **battery** is working. Try it on a spare buzzer or light.

2. Check that all the parts are in **the right place and connected the right way** round.

3. If a circuit that used to work stops working, **see if something has come loose.**

4. If your circuit still doesn't work, **ask for help.**

Fault finding

What to do if your circuit doesn't work

Before you ask for help, look carefully at your circuit:

1. Check that the **battery** is working. Try it on a spare buzzer or light.

2. Check that all the parts are in **the right place and connected the right way** round.

3. If a circuit that used to work stops working, **see if something has come loose.**

4. If your circuit still doesn't work, **ask for help.**

TOP LAYER

Staple this end

TOP LAYER

MIDDLE LAYER

Remember: Do not put glue where strips cross.

Staple switch together here

| | | CUT OUT | | | CUT OUT | | | CUT OUT | |

| | | CUT OUT | | | CUT OUT | | | CUT OUT | |

BOTTOM LAYER

Remember: Do not put glue where strips cross.

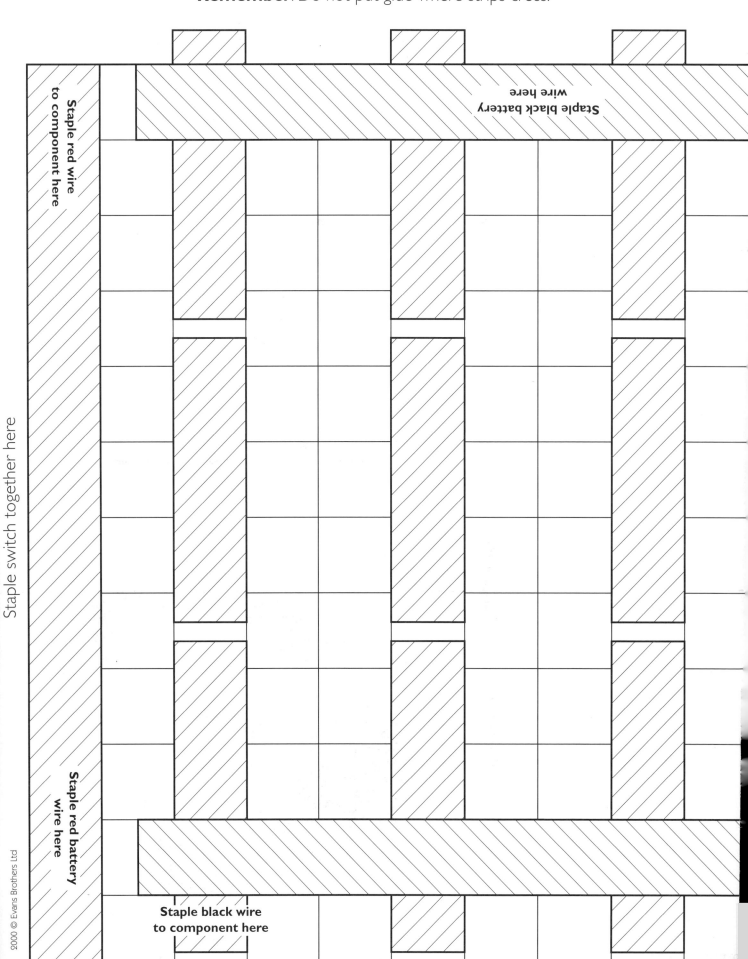

Staple red wire
to component here

Staple black battery
wire here

Staple switch together here

Staple red battery
wire here

Staple black wire
to component here

2000 © Evans Brothers Ltd

Machine support structure template
Amazing Machines page 6

Cut line

Cut line

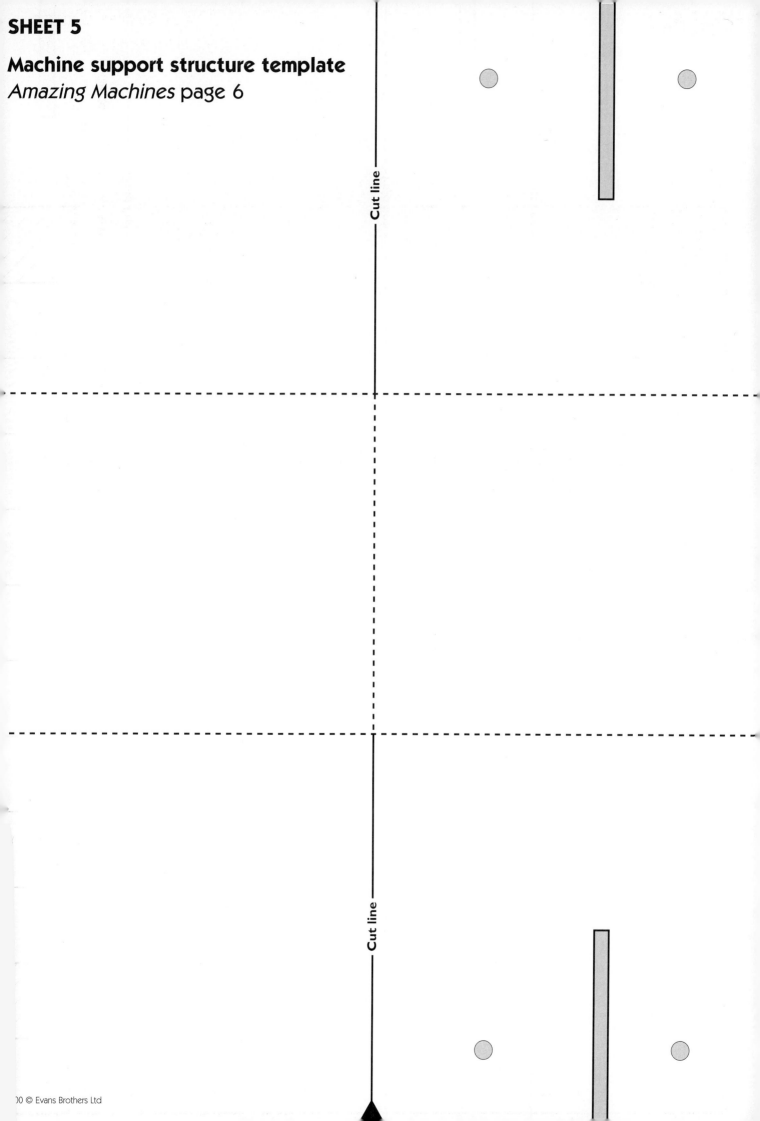

SHEET 6

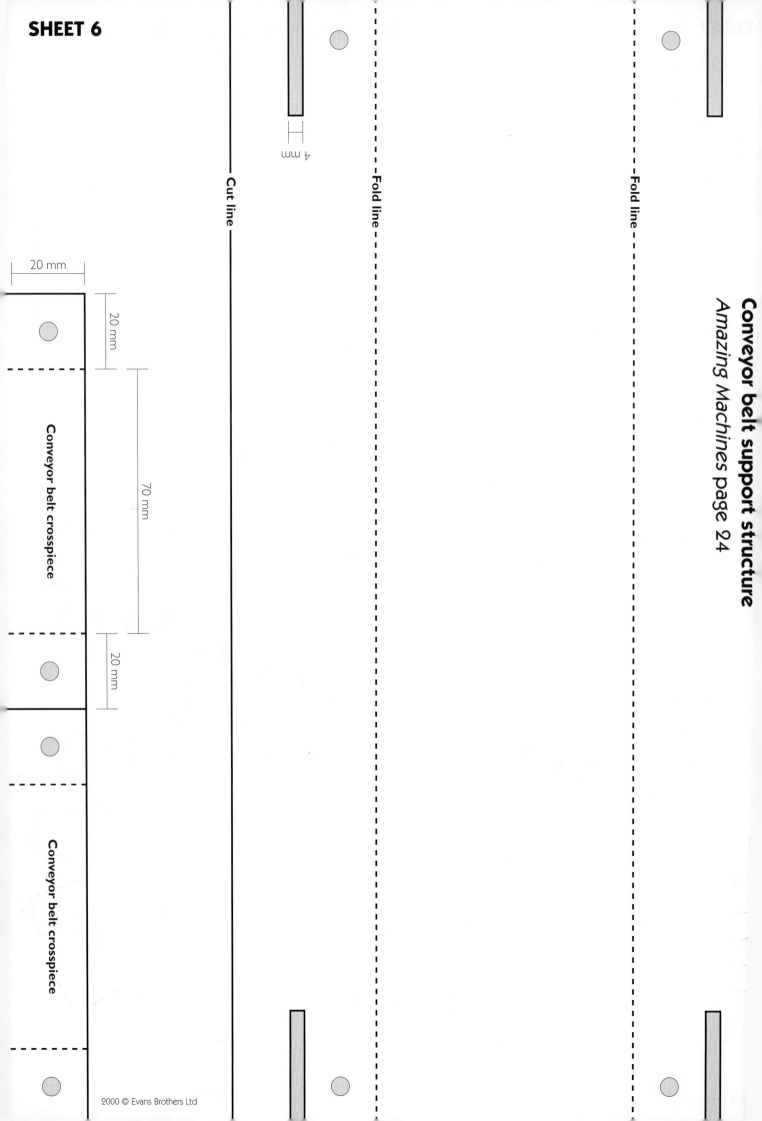

Cut line

Fold line

Fold line

4 mm

20 mm

20 mm

70 mm

20 mm

Conveyor belt crosspiece

Conveyor belt crosspiece

Note: *For gear wheels to work together, the teeth must be the same size.*

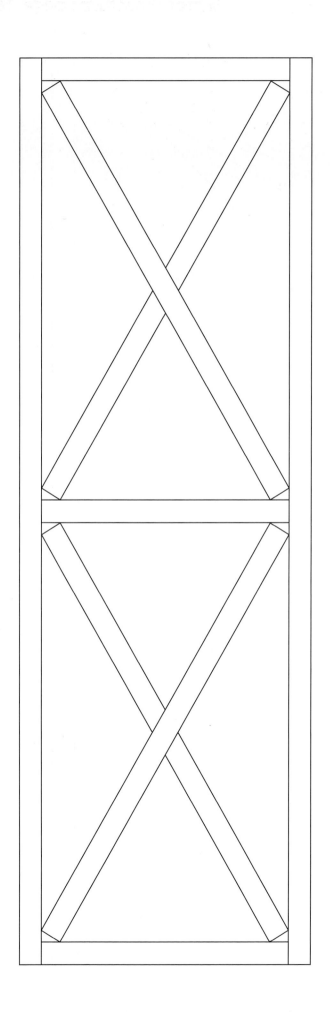
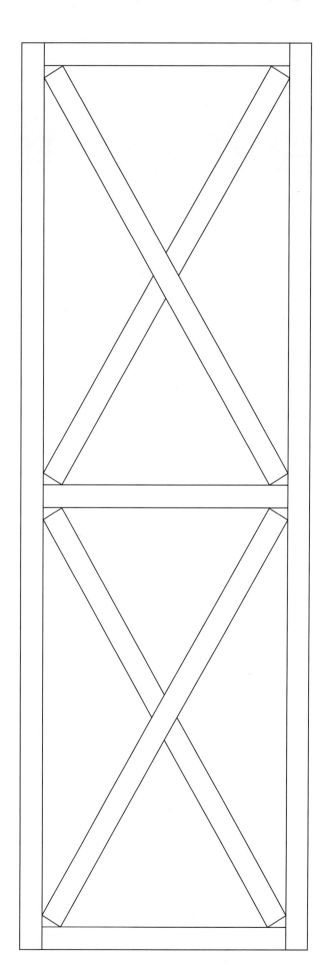

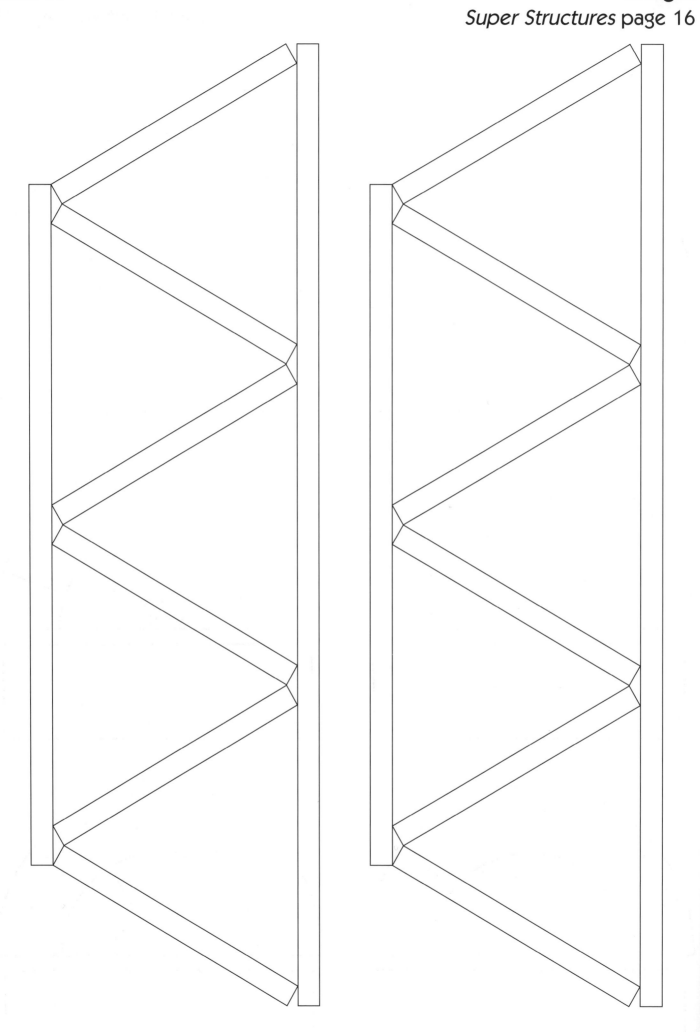

You can also enlarge this plan if larger
bridges are wanted.

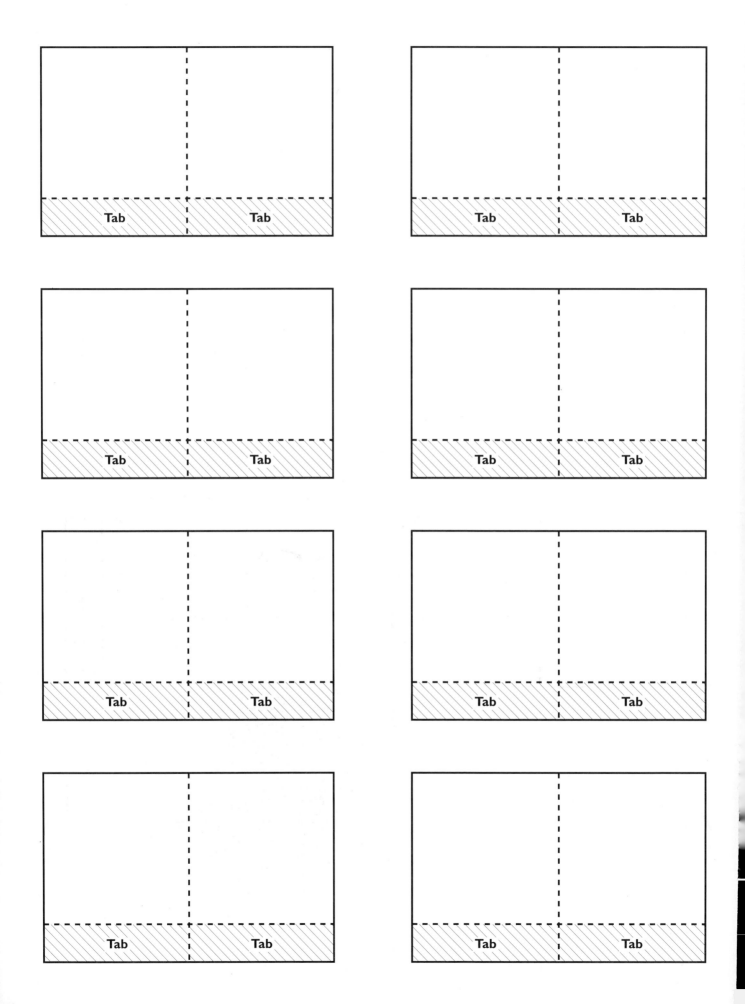

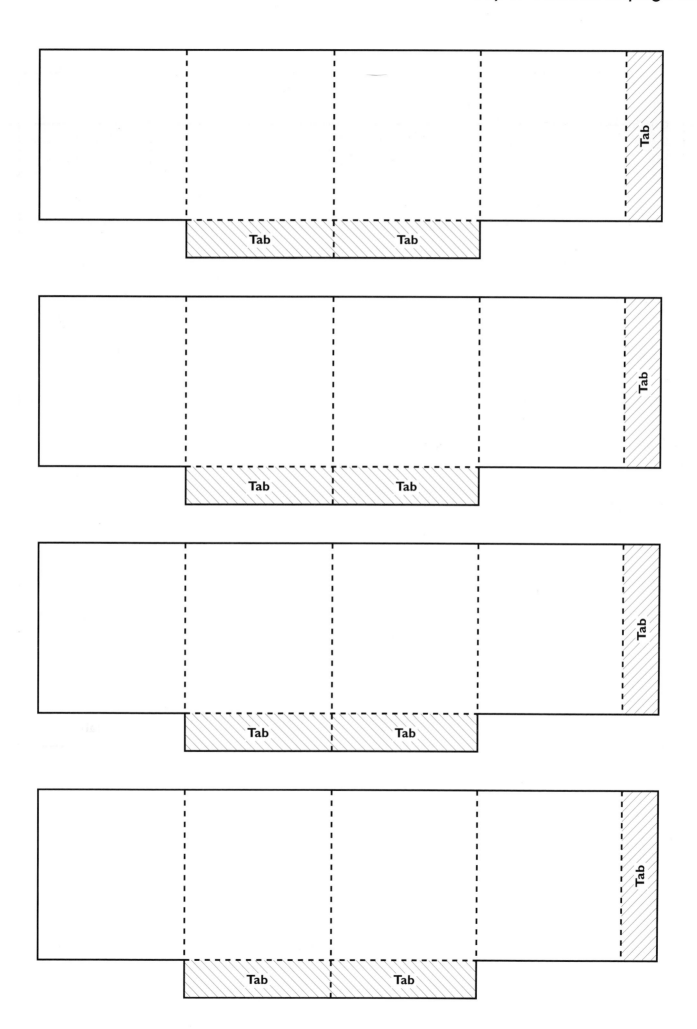

Structures that protect

Super Structures page 26

Cut line

Fold line

CUT OUT

CUT OUT

You can enlarge this plan if larger
bags are wanted.

Cut line ─────

─────── **Fold line** ─────────────────

**Make this the inside to
hide the fold lines**

2000 © Evans Brothers Ltd

Tab (stick here)

CUT OUT

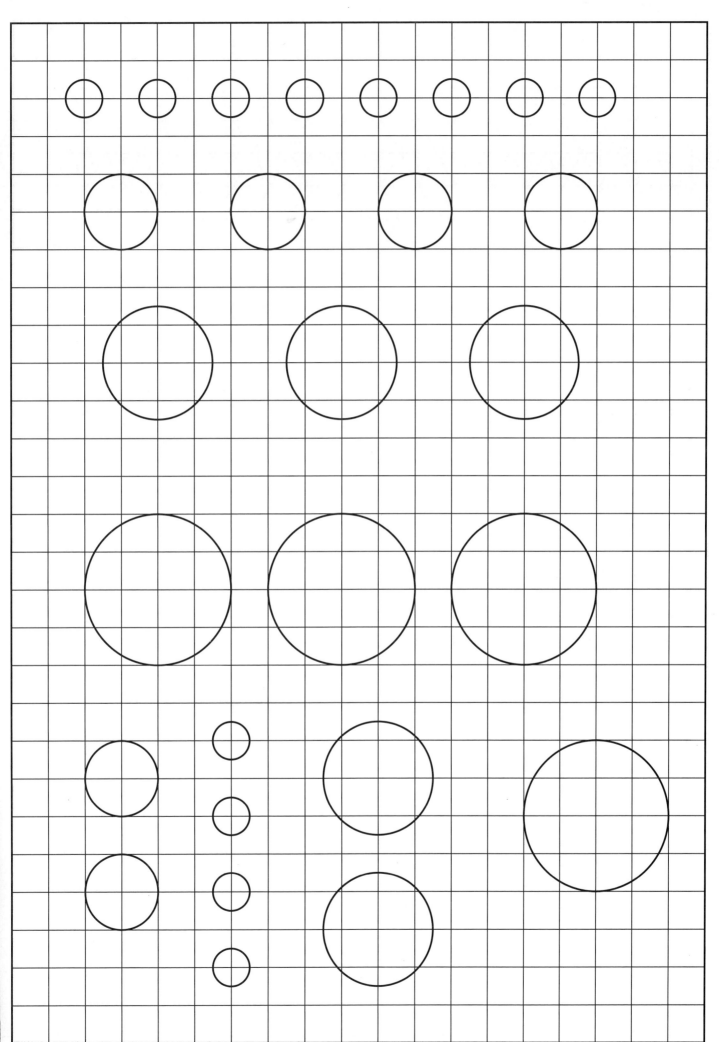

This way up

This way up

Design Challenge Record Sheet Part 1

Name:	Date:

My design challenge was to design and make…

I think a good project like this should…

Include what you would like it to do.

Things I found out to help me have ideas…

Say where you looked for information.

My first ideas were like this…

Use an extra sheet of plain paper if you need more space.